THIS BEN 10™ ANNUAL BELONGS TO

Ben 16

CONTENTS

EGMONT

We bring stories to life

First published in Great Britain 2008 by Egmont UK Limited
239 Kensington High Street, London W8 6SA
Cartoon Network, the logo, BEN 10 and all related characters and elements
are trademark and © Cartoon Network
(s08)
All rights reserved.

ISBN 978 1 4052 3909 7
3 5 7 9 10 8 6 4 2
Printed in Italy

BEN TENNYSON

Accidental Hero

BEN WAS LOOKING FORWARD TO A SUMMER SPENT ON THE ROAD WITH HIS GRANDPA MAX – UNTIL HIS ANNOYING COUSIN GWEN SHOWED UP! STILL, A VERY SPECIAL DISCOVERY WILL MAKE IT A SUMMER LIKE NO OTHER ...

PERSONALITY

BEN'S A TYPICAL 10-YEAR-OLD BOY. HE'S INTO PLAYING SUMO SLAMMERS, AND GOOFING ABOUT. HOWEVER HARD HE TRIES (NOT VERY HARD!), BEN CAN'T STAY OUT OF MISCHIEF.

STRENGTHS

BEN'S FIERCELY LOYAL, AND WILL DO WHATEVER HE CAN TO PROTECT HIS FAMILY FROM HARM. HE'S ALSO PRETTY FEARLESS – EVEN WHEN HE DOESN'T HAVE AN ALIEN HERO TO BACK HIM UP!

WEAKNESSES

BEN TENDS TO RUSH INTO THINGS WITHOUT THINKING. HE'S A BIG SHOW-OFF AND LOVES THE ATTENTION THE OMNITRIX BRINGS HIM. HE'S ALSO BEEN KNOWN TO USE IT FOR PRANKS ...

THE OMNITRIX

Box of Trix

AFTER IT CRASH-LANDS ON EARTH, THE OMNITRIX ATTACHES ITSELF TO BEN'S WRIST – AND WON'T COME OFF! SINCE THERE'S NO INSTRUCTION MANUAL, BEN HAS TO WORK OUT HOW TO USE IT BY HIMSELF ...

FUNCTION

THE OMNITRIX IS AN ADVANCED ALIEN DEVICE, WHICH ALLOWS THE WEARER TO TURN THEMSELVES INTO THE ALIEN OF THEIR CHOICE FOR A SHORT TIME.

DEFECTS

THE OMNITRIX DOESN'T ALWAYS TURN BEN INTO THE ALIEN HE WANTS, AND SOMETIMES REFUSES TO WORK AT ALL. IT ALSO TAKES TIME TO RECHARGE AFTER EACH TRANSFORMATION.

ENHANCEMENTS

AT FIRST, THE OMNITRIX ONLY GIVES BEN 10 ALIENS. BUT IT HAS MORE SECRET POWERS THAT HE WILL UNLOCK OVER TIME. UNFORTUNATELY, BEN'S ENEMIES KNOW MORE ABOUT IT THAN HE DOES ...

PART 1

BEN 10 FAST LANE

MAN OF ACTION *writer* DARIO BRIZUELA *artist*
STUDIO 1137 *letterer* HEROIC AGE *colorist*
RACHEL GLUCKSTERN *asst. editor* JOAN HILTY *editor*
BEN 10 *created by* MAN OF ACTION

THEY'RE *AMAZING*, GRADY! HOW FAST ARE THEY GOING?

UP TO TWO HUNDRED AND TEN MILES AN HOUR, GWEN!

MY OLD FRIEND *GRADY* WAS NICE ENOUGH TO INVITE US.

I THOUGHT YOU MIGHT APPRECIATE A LITTLE FUEL-INJECTED FUN AFTER MONDAY'S DEBACLE AT THE LOUISIANAN *ANT FARM.*

WHAT DO *YOU* THINK, BEN?

...I THINK MY EARS ARE BLEEDING.

DON'T TELL ME YOU'RE *BORED*, BEN? LOOK AT THOSE FEATS OF HUMAN ENGINEERING! IT TAKES A LOT OF *SKILL* TO BE A RACECAR DRIVER!

SKILL? ALL THEY DO IS DRIVE AROUND IN A CIRCLE!

VROOM

SHOOTING STAR

WOW-- 218.432 SECONDS! THAT'S A TRACK RECORD!

BILL ELLIOT ONLY DID 210.386, AND THAT WAS *BEFORE* THE CARBURETOR RESTRICTIONS--

HOW COULD YOU EVEN POSSIBLY KNOW THAT? YOU'RE A *GIRL!*

SHE'S RIGHT, BEN! AND ON ANY OTHER DAY THAT WOULD BE A TRACK RECORD, BUT TODAY, WE'RE JUST LUCKY.

HUH? YOU'VE GOT THE FINEST CAR OUT HERE. WHAT ELSE COULD POSSIBLY GO UP AGAINST HER?

--UH, WHAT IS *THAT!*

SPEAK OF THE DEVIL... AND HE SHOWS HIS TAILPIPE.

RUUUMMMBLE

CONTINUED ON PAGE 18

13

GWEN TENNYSON

Voice of Reason

GWEN IS BEN'S COUSIN. SHE CAN'T UNDERSTAND WHY THE COOLEST GADGET IN THE GALAXY ENDED UP ON THE WRIST OF THE BIGGEST DWEEB IN THE GALAXY. BUT EVEN SHE HAS TO ADMIT THAT BEN DOES GOOD SOMETIMES ...

PERSONALITY

GWEN TRIES TO KEEP BEN FROM GOING TOO WILD. SHE THINKS AHEAD, AND TRIES TO STOP BEN GETTING INTO TROUBLE (USUALLY WITHOUT SUCCESS). SHE IS AS SENSIBLE AS BEN IS MISCHIEVOUS.

STRENGTHS

GWEN HAS A STRONG NATURAL TALENT FOR MAGIC – SHE'S GOOD WITH MAGICAL OBJECTS AND SPELLS. SHE ALSO HAS MARTIAL ARTS SKILLS, AND SHE'S HANDY WITH MACHINES.

WEAKNESSES

GWEN HAS A TENDENCY TO THINK SHE'S RIGHT ALL THE TIME. EVEN WHEN SHE IS, IT'S PRETTY ANNOYING! SHE ALSO GETS JEALOUS WHEN BEN HOGS ALL THE ATTENTION.

MAX TENNYSON
Adventurous Senior

MAX IS BEN AND GWEN'S 60-YEAR-OLD GRANDPA. HE CAN'T WAIT TO TAKE THEM ON A SUMMER ADVENTURE IN HIS MOTORHOME. BUT HE HAS NO IDEA WHAT AN ADVENTURE IT WILL BE ...

PERSONALITY

MAX HAS A REAL TASTE FOR ADVENTURE, AND WANTS BEN AND GWEN TO SHARE IN THE FUN. HE ALSO HAS A TASTE FOR WEIRD FOOD – SOMETHING THEY AREN'T SO KEEN TO SHARE!

STRENGTHS

MAX HAS A GOOD KNOWLEDGE OF ALIENS, WEAPONS AND TECHNOLOGY – IN FACT, A SUSPICIOUSLY GOOD KNOWLEDGE, SEEING AS HE CLAIMS HE USED TO BE A PLUMBER ...

WEAKNESSES

IS MAX HIDING SOMETHING FROM HIS GRANDKIDS? THERE'S DEFINITELY SOMETHING ABOUT HIS PAST THAT DOESN'T ADD UP, AND BEN AND GWEN WANT TO KNOW THE TRUTH.

CRYSTAL MAZE

DID SOMEONE CALL FOR A PETROSAPIEN? HELP BEN GO DIAMONDHEAD BY STEPPING ON CRYSTALS IN THIS ORDER ...

YOU CAN GO UP, DOWN, LEFT OR RIGHT – BUT NOT DIAGONALLY!

START

FINISH

FREAKIN' OUT

MOST OF THESE GHOSTFREAKS ARE EVEN MORE FREAKY THAN USUAL! CAN YOU CIRCLE THE TWO THAT ARE THE SAME?

A

B

C

D

E

F

NAME GAME

1. TAKE THE LETTERS SHOWN FROM THE NAMES OF EACH OF THESE ALIENS ...

4TH LETTER, 7TH LETTER

GREY MATTER

6TH LETTER

DIAMONDHEAD

6TH LETTER, 10TH LETTER

GHOSTFREAK

6TH LETTER

HEATBLAST

2ND LETTER, 7TH LETTER

RIPJAWS

LOOK THROUGH THE ANNUAL FOR MORE CLUES.

2. WRITE THEM DOWN HERE.

3. NOW UNJUMBLE THEM TO SPELL THE NAME OF ANOTHER ALIEN!

SUDOTRIX

FILL IN THIS GRID SO THAT EACH LINE AND 4X4 SQUARE HAS ONE OF EACH OMNITRIX SYMBOL IN IT.

ANSWERS ON PAGE 69

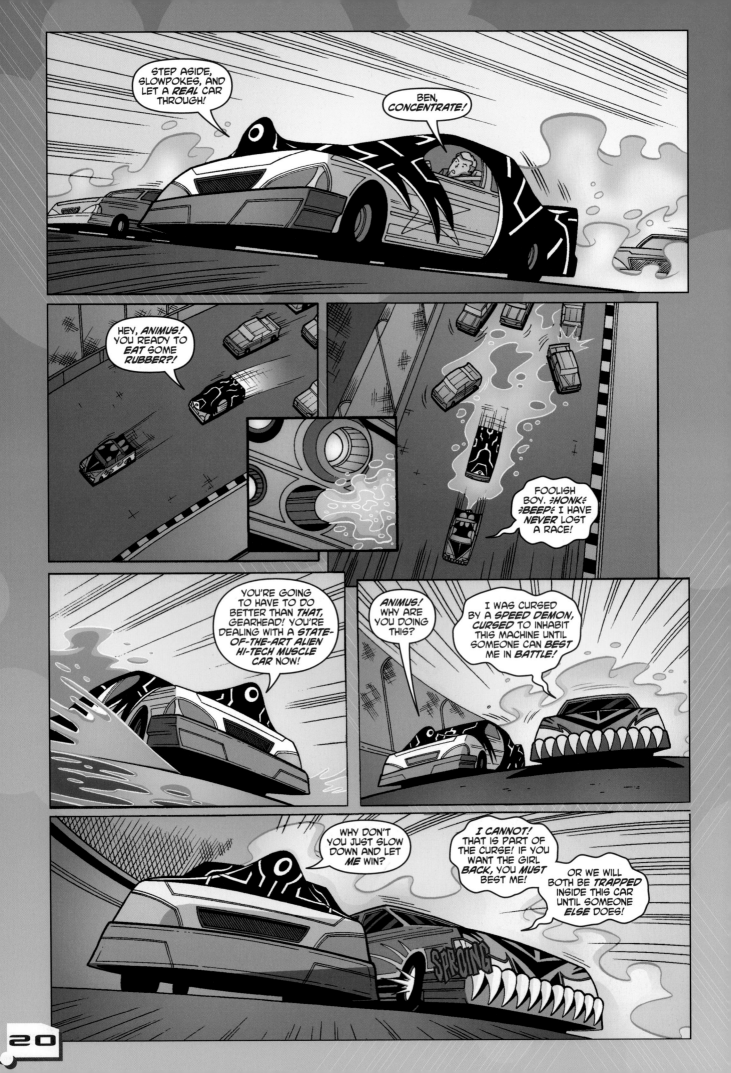

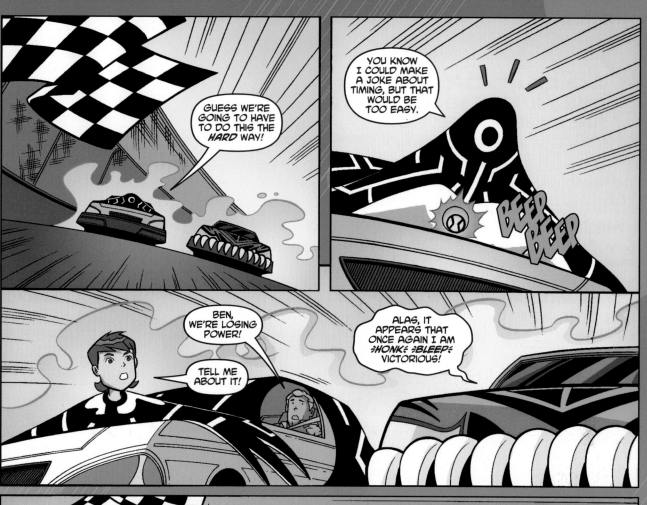

SHUTDOWN

HELP GREY MATTER TAKE DOWN AN ALIEN ROBOT FROM THE INSIDE! FOLLOW THE WIRES TO FIND THE NUMBERED BOX THAT IS LINKED TO ALL THE OTHERS TO TAKE OUT THE CENTRAL BATTERY. WHICH ONE IS IT?

THE NEED FOR SPEED

HOW MANY TIMES CAN YOU FIND XLR8 IN THIS WORDSEARCH? READ IN ANY DIRECTION.

L	R	X	R	R	L	8	8
X	L	R	8	8	X	8	X
R	X	8	L	R	L	L	R
L	8	L	X	L	R	8	R
8	R	L	X	X	8	L	L
X	L	8	X	R	R	X	8
R	X	X	L	X	L	R	8
L	8	X	L	R	L	L	R

ANSWERS ON PAGE 69

23

VILGAX

Alien Overlord

VILGAX IS A RUTHLESS, INTERGALACTIC CONQUEROR – AND HE WANTS THE OMNITRIX! ONCE HE HAS IT, HE WILL USE ITS POWERS TO UNLEASH A DEVASTATING REIGN OF TERROR. THAT'S BAD NEWS FOR EVERYONE!

THE BAD GUYS

PERSONALITY

VILGAX IS A TYPICAL MONSTROUS SPACE TYRANT. HIS HOBBIES INCLUDE DESTROYING WORLDS, ENSLAVING POPULATIONS, AND SCOURGING THE GALAXY WITH A STORM OF PURE EVIL.

STRENGTHS

VILGAX WILL STOP AT NOTHING IN HIS DETERMINATION TO GET THE OMNITRIX. CARING NOTHING FOR HUMAN LIFE, HE USES HIS COLOSSAL STRENGTH TO CRUSH ALL WHO STAND IN HIS WAY.

WEAKNESSES

WHEN HE IS SERIOUSLY WOUNDED IN A SPACE BATTLE, VILGAX MUST REMAIN SUSPENDED IN A REGENERATION TANK. HOWEVER, HE HAS NO SHORTAGE OF MINIONS TO DO HIS BIDDING.

KEVIN 11

Angry Young Man

KEVIN IS A REBELLIOUS 11-YEAR-OLD BOY. BUT HE'S ALSO A MUTANT, CAPABLE OF ABSORBING ANY TYPE OF ENERGY – AS BEN FINDS OUT WHEN HE TRIES TO USE THE OMNITRIX'S ALIENS AGAINST HIM ...

PERSONALITY

KEVIN IS EVERYTHING BEN IS NOT – HE'S DECEITFUL, SELFISH, AND GETS A KICK OUT OF HURTING PEOPLE. HE THINKS THE WORLD IS OUT TO GET HIM – AND HE WANTS REVENGE!

STRENGTHS

KEVIN'S KEY STRENGTH IS HIS ABILITY TO USE OTHER PEOPLE'S POWERS AGAINST THEM. WHEN BEN TRIES TO FIGHT HIM, KEVIN BECOMES A HYBRID OF 10 ALIENS AND HIMSELF!

WEAKNESSES

AS A FUSION OF ALIENS, KEVIN DOESN'T HAVE THE FULL POWERS OF ANY OF THEM. WORSE, KEVIN IS INCAPABLE OF CO-OPERATING WITH ANYONE, EVEN WHEN IT WOULD HELP HIM OUT.

BEN! CAN WE *STOP* WITH THE BLINDING FLASHES OF LIGHT ALREADY?

SORRY.

THAT WAS *NO* GORILLA, THOUGH.

MAKES SENSE. ARE YOU *SURE?*

WILDMUTT'S *INFRARED VISION* SHOWED A *GUY* INSIDE THAT GORILLA SUIT--

--AND I BET I KNOW *WHO!*

REALLY? IT'D BE NICE TO PUT AT LEAST *ONE* OF THESE CROOKS OUT OF BUSINESS...

OH, I CAN DO BETTER THAN *THAT*--

--I CAN SHUT 'EM *ALL* DOWN!

FOUR ARMS

Species: Tetramand

POWERFUL TETRAMANDS ARE 3 METRES TALL, WITH FOUR MIGHTY ARMS AND TOUGH, ARMOURED SKIN. THEIR BIGGEST STRENGTH IS JUST THAT – THEIR STRENGTH! BUT THEY CAN ALSO BE DANGEROUSLY CLUMSY.

A GOOD TIME TO GO FOUR ARMS:
WHENEVER SUPERHUMAN FIGHTING POWER IS NEEDED – FOUR ARMS HAS PLENTY!

A BAD TIME TO GO FOUR ARMS:
WHEN STEALTH AND CUNNING ARE NEEDED – TETRAMANDS DON'T DO SNEAKY!

HOMEWORLD: KHOROS
A SCORCHED, DUSTY WORLD WHERE EVERY DAY IS A BATTLE FOR SURVIVAL.

SCALE

BEN   FOUR ARMS

STINKFLY
Species: Lepidopterran

LEPIDOPTERRANS ARE LARGE, INTELLIGENT INSECTS, SKILLED IN ACROBATIC FLYING. THEY FIGHT WITH GOOS AND GASES MADE INSIDE THEIR BODIES, BUT THEIR FRAGILE WINGS ARE VULNERABLE TO ATTACK.

A GOOD TIME TO GO STINKFLY:

FOR EXPLORING LARGE AREAS OR DARING AERIAL RESCUES, A FAST AGILE LEPIDOPTERRAN IS THE PERFECT ALIEN.

A BAD TIME TO GO STINKFLY:

WATCH OUT FOR POISONOUS GAS – ONE SNIFF COULD GROUND STINKFLY FOR GOOD!

HOMEWORLD: LEPIDOPTERRA

A LUSH SWAMP PLANET WHERE INSECTS LIVE IN HARMONY AMONGST MANY DIFFERENT GIANT PLANTS.

SCALE

BEN   STINKFLY

BEN WANTED TO GO HEATBLAST TO PUT OUT A FIRE, BUT HE GOT FOUR ARMS INSTEAD! NEVER MIND – IF HE PULLS DOWN A WATER TOWER, THE DRY RIVER BEDS WILL LEAD THE WATER TO THE FLAMES. BUT WHICH COLOUR WATER TOWER WILL PUT OUT ALL THE FIRES? (REMEMBER, WATER ONLY FLOWS DOWNHILL – DUH!)

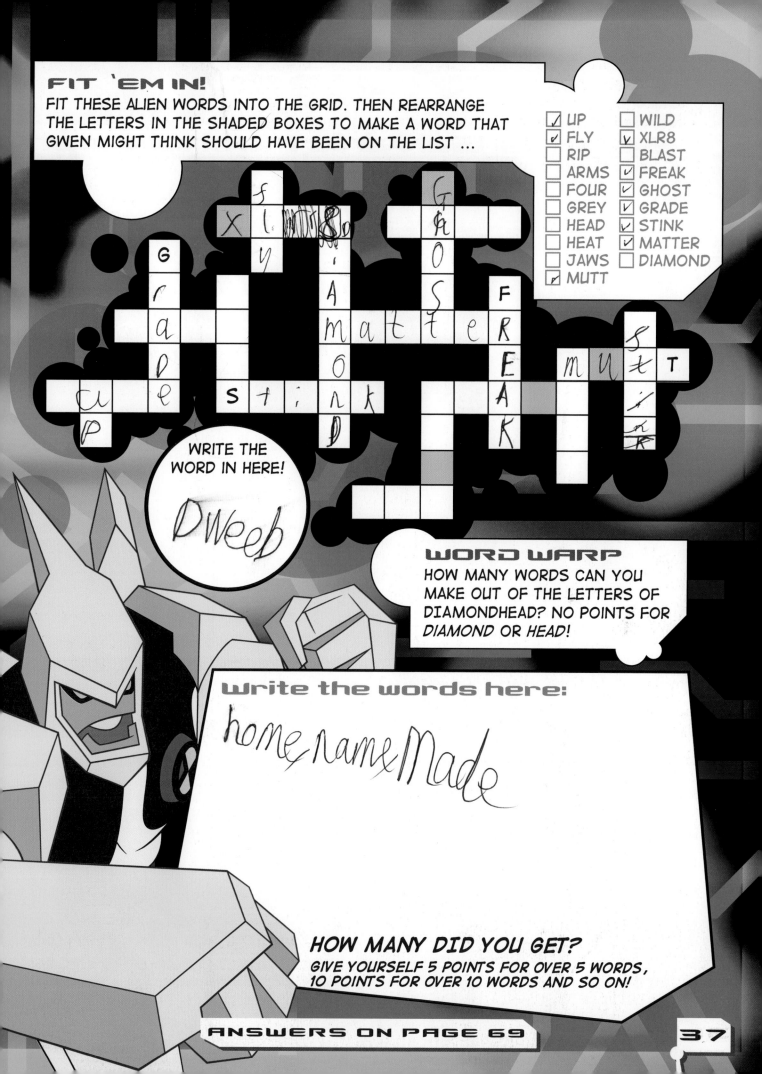

FIT 'EM IN!

FIT THESE ALIEN WORDS INTO THE GRID. THEN REARRANGE THE LETTERS IN THE SHADED BOXES TO MAKE A WORD THAT GWEN MIGHT THINK SHOULD HAVE BEEN ON THE LIST ...

- ☑ UP
- ☑ FLY
- ☐ RIP
- ☐ ARMS
- ☐ FOUR
- ☐ GREY
- ☐ HEAD
- ☐ HEAT
- ☐ JAWS
- ☑ MUTT
- ☐ WILD
- ☑ XLR8
- ☐ BLAST
- ☑ FREAK
- ☑ GHOST
- ☑ GRADE
- ☑ STINK
- ☑ MATTER
- ☐ DIAMOND

WRITE THE WORD IN HERE!

Dweeb

WORD WARP

HOW MANY WORDS CAN YOU MAKE OUT OF THE LETTERS OF DIAMONDHEAD? NO POINTS FOR *DIAMOND* OR *HEAD*!

write the words here:

home name Made

HOW MANY DID YOU GET?
GIVE YOURSELF 5 POINTS FOR OVER 5 WORDS, 10 POINTS FOR OVER 10 WORDS AND SO ON!

ANSWERS ON PAGE 69

UPGRADE

Species: Galvanic Mechomorph

GALVANIC MECHOMORPHS ARE LIVING MACHINES WITH LIQUID METAL SKINS AND BODIES FORMED OF TINY ORGANIC CIRCUITS. THEY CAN MERGE WITH ANY PIECE OF TECH, BRINGING IT TO LIFE UNDER THEIR CONTROL.

A GOOD TIME TO GO UPGRADE:

UPGRADE CAN TURN ANY MACHINE, HOWEVER HARMLESS, INTO AN EFFECTIVE WEAPON.

A BAD TIME TO GO UPGRADE:

MECHOMORPHS CAN'T AFFECT LIVING TISSUE. AND THEY DON'T LIKE ELECTROMAGNETIC SURGES!

HOMEWORLD: GALVAN B

A MINERAL-RICH MOON, BROUGHT TO LIFE ACCIDENTALLY BY ROGUE NANO-TECHNOLOGY.

SCALE

BEN   UPGRADE

38

WILDMUTT

Species: Vulpimancer

SLATHERING, SNARLING BALLS OF FUR AND CLAWS, SAVAGE VULPIMANCERS ARE DEFINITELY NOT PETS! VULPIMANCERS ARE BLIND, BUT HEIGHTENED SMELL AND HEAT VISION GIVE THEM PLENTY OF BITE.

A GOOD TIME TO GO WILDMUTT:

WHEN ANIMAL INSTINCTS ARE CALLED FOR, WILDMUTT WILL SNIFF OUT THE ENEMY AND HUNT IT DOWN, WHATEVER IT TAKES.

A BAD TIME TO GO WILDMUTT:

DON'T FORGET, WILDMUTT IS A BEAST – REASONING, STRATEGY AND SPEECH ARE BEYOND HIM.

HOMEWORLD: VULPIN

A BARREN TOXIC-WASTE DUMP, SAVAGERY IS A WAY OF LIFE ON THIS WORLD.

SCALE

BEN   WILDMUTT

39

TO THE RESCUE

GWEN'S IN TROUBLE! YOU NEED TO GET TO HER FAST. STARTING FROM GRANDPA, PASS THROUGH EACH ALIEN ONCE, IN THE DIRECTION OF THE ARROW. YOU CAN GO THROUGH THE ROBOT DRONES, BUT YOU CAN'T GO DOWN THE SAME PATH TWICE.

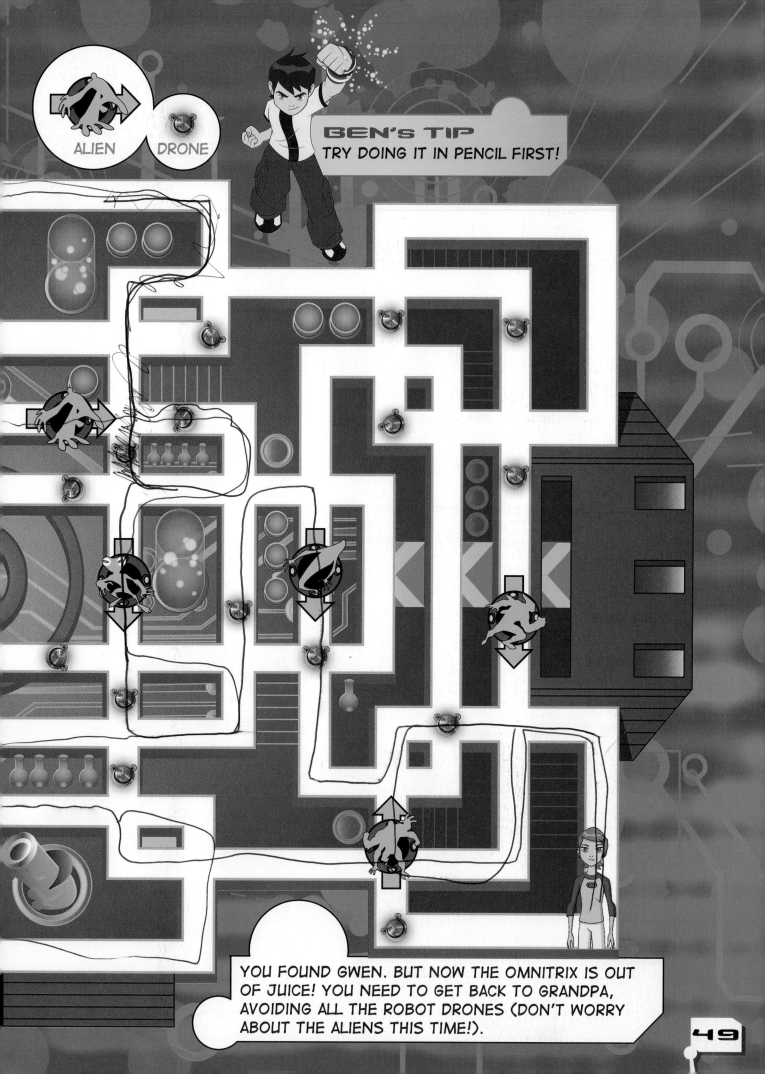

ALIEN   DRONE

BEN'S TIP
TRY DOING IT IN PENCIL FIRST!

YOU FOUND GWEN. BUT NOW THE OMNITRIX IS OUT
OF JUICE! YOU NEED TO GET BACK TO GRANDPA,
AVOIDING ALL THE ROBOT DRONES (DON'T WORRY
ABOUT THE ALIENS THIS TIME!).

DIAMONDHEAD

Species: Petrosapien

PETROSAPIENS ARE MADE OF LIVING ROCK. THEY'RE VIRTUALLY INDESTRUCTIBLE, AND THEIR JAGGED LIMBS TEAR THROUGH METAL LIKE IT WAS PAPER. THEY CAN ALSO FIRE A DEVASTATING BARRAGE OF CRYSTAL SHARDS.

A GOOD TIME TO GO DIAMONDHEAD:

DIAMONDHEAD CAN TAKE A LOT OF PUNISHMENT, AND GIVE IT BACK – HIS BODY REFLECTS BEAM WEAPONS.

A BAD TIME TO GO DIAMONDHEAD:

A POWERFUL SOUNDBLAST AT THE RIGHT FREQUENCY COULD SHATTER DIAMONDHEAD – FOREVER!

HOMEWORLD: PETROPIA

A CRAGGY CRYSTALLINE WORLD INHABITED BY RACES OF GEM-BASED SILICON BEINGS.

SCALE

BEN   DIAMONDHEAD

GHOSTFREAK

Species: Ectonurite

THESE PHANTOMS WILL GIVE YOU NIGHTMARES! AS WELL AS LOOKING SCARY, THEY CAN ALSO FLOAT THROUGH WALLS, BECOME INVISIBLE, AND EVEN POSSESS OTHER BODIES FOR A SHORT WHILE!

A GOOD TIME TO GO GHOSTFREAK:

NIGHTTIME! ECTONURITES ARE MORE POWERFUL IN THE DARK AND A LOT MORE TERRIFYING!

A BAD TIME TO GO GHOSTFREAK:

ENEMIES WHO USE FEAR AS A WEAPON THEMSELVES WON'T BE FREAKED BY GHOSTFREAK.

HOMEWORLD: ANUR PHAETOS

NO TRAVELLER HAS EVER RETURNED FROM THIS MYSTERIOUS DARK REALM.

SCALE

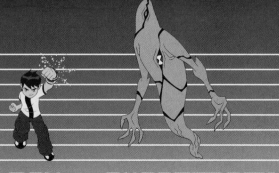

BEN   GHOSTFREAK

STORMFRONT

GETTING TO THE ISLAND OUT AT SEA WOULD HAVE BEEN A BREEZE WITH RIPJAWS. UNFORTUNATELY, BEN WENT STINKFLY – AND THERE'S A STORM BREWING! WHERE SHOULD BEN TAKE OFF SO THE STRONG WINDS BLOW HIM TO THE ISLAND? STARTING AT THE DIFFERENT PLACES, MOVE THE NUMBER SHOWN IN THE DIRECTION OF THE ARROW TO SEE IF YOU REACH THE ISLAND.

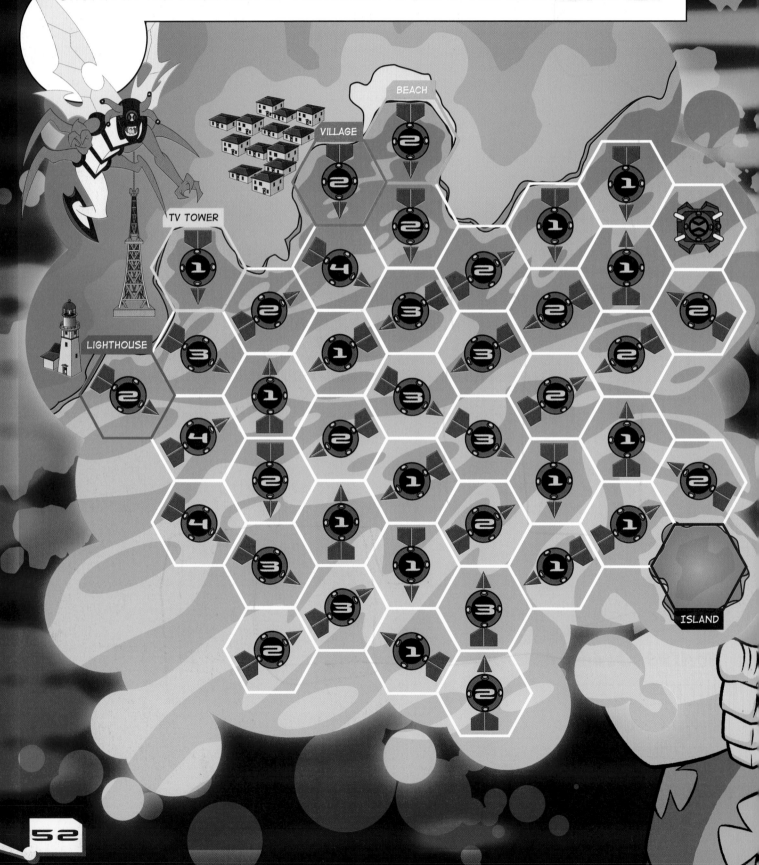

UP CLOSE
ONE OF THESE CLOSE-UPS DOES NOT QUITE MATCH THE PICTURE. WHICH ONE IS IT?

GROSS OUT!
GRANDPA HAS COOKED UP A DELICIOUS PLATE OF GRUBS! HOW MANY ARE THERE ON HIS PLATE?

ANSWERS ON PAGE 69

THERE'S ROOM F'R ONE MORE, PARDNER! AHHAHAHAHAHA!!
AAAAAAAAAH!!
YOU'RE KIDDING. THAT SCARED YOU?!
YOU CAN SEE THE WIRES! AND THAT DIALOGUE--! PUH-LEASE!
YOU'RE JUST TOO DUMB TO BE SCARED, BEN TENNYSON!
I HAPPEN TO HAVE A HIGHLY DEVELOPED INTELLECT, WHICH ACCOUNTS FOR--
GAAAAH!
ACCOUNTS FOR YOU BEING A WEENIE! BWAHH HA!
THAT'S NOT VERY NICE.
DON'T WORRY, GWEN CAN HANDLE A SCARE-- SHE HAS TO LOOK AT HERSELF IN THE MIRROR EVERY DAY.
BESIDES...
BEING SCARED NEVER HURT ANYONE.
FWOOOSH!

CONTINUED ON PAGE 62

GREY MATTER

Species: Galvan

THEY'RE NOT BIG, BUT THEY ARE CLEVER! DESPITE BEING ONLY 12 CM TALL, GALVANS POSSESS SOME OF THE MOST SOPHISTICATED TECH IN THE GALAXY. PLUS THEY CAN SQUEEZE INTO TINY SPACES AND STICK TO ANY SURFACE.

A GOOD TIME TO GO GREY MATTER:

GREY MATTER CAN SLIP INSIDE A MACHINE UNNOTICED, AND OPERATE IT FROM WITHIN.

A BAD TIME TO GO GREY MATTER:

IN A CROWD, TINY GREY MATTER COULD EASILY FIND HIMSELF GETTING TRAMPLED UNDERFOOT!

HOMEWORLD: GALVAN PRIME

A HI-TECH WORLD BLANKETED WITH MINIATURE CITIES AND TRANSPORT NETWORKS.

SCALE

BEN   GREY MATTER

XLR8

Species: Kineceleran

KINECELERANS LIVE LIFE IN THE FAST LANE. BY MANIPULATING FRICTION AND CHANNELLING STATIC ELECTRICITY THEY CAN RUN AT UP TO 800 KM/H. AT THAT SPEED THERE'S VERY LITTLE TIME TO THINK!

A GOOD TIME TO GO XLR8:

FEEL THE NEED FOR SPEED? XLR8 CAN TIE AN OPPONENT IN KNOTS BEFORE HE'S EVEN HAD TIME TO BLINK!

A BAD TIME TO GO XLR8:

MUD, ICE AND WATER MAKE THE GOING DIFFICULT FOR XLR8. AND SO DO MAGNETS!

HOMEWORLD: KINET

A RAPIDLY ORBITING WORLD WHERE LIFE IS LIVED AT AN ACCELERATED PACE.

SCALE

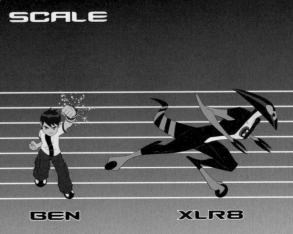

BEN   XLR8

SPOOKY CHANGES?

THERE ARE SOME DIFFERENCES BETWEEN THESE TWO CREEPY PICTURES - 10 OF 'EM (NATURALLY!). CAN YOU SPOT THEM ALL?

ANSWERS ON PAGE 69

WISH YOU WERE HERE?

GWEN'S BORING POSTCARD CONTAINS ALL THE NUMBERS FROM ONE TO TEN. CAN YOU FIND THEM ALL? WE'VE DONE ONE FOR YOU.

Dear Aunt Vera,

Sorry if I've not written in a while! Yesterday we visited the Hiawassi Xylophone Museum – it was even better than I expected! It would be no lie to say it was the high point of our holiday. Then in East Ellijay I bought an enormous basket – who knew something made with reeds could weigh that much!

Lots of love,
Gwen

Aunt Vera

Shady Buttes Retirement

Community

Tombstone, AZ 85638

ADD 'EM UPGRADE!

CAN YOU FILL IN THIS NUMBER PYRAMID? TWO NUMBERS NEXT TO EACH OTHER MUST ADD UP TO THE NUMBER ABOVE THEM. GET GOING!

HEATBLAST

Species: Pyronite

PYRONITES ARE HOT STUFF – LITERALLY! MADE OF RED-HOT MAGMA, THEY CAN CHANNEL VAST AMOUNTS OF HEAT THROUGH THEIR BODIES, AND SHOOT OUT SEARING FLAMES. THEY CAN ALSO ABSORB HEAT TO PUT OUT FIRES.

A GOOD TIME TO GO HEATBLAST:

WITH HIS MASTERY OF FIRE, RAGING INFERNOS ARE NO MATCH FOR HEATBLAST.

A BAD TIME TO GO HEATBLAST:

TOO MUCH COLD WATER COULD EXTINGUISH HEATBLAST'S SPARK FOR GOOD.

HOMEWORLD: PYROS

A VAST SUNSCAPE, WITH SOLAR FLARES AND RIVERS OF LAVA STRETCHING TO THE HORIZON.

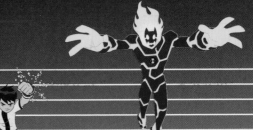

SCALE

BEN   HEATBLAST

RIPJAWS

Species: Piscciss Volanns

SNAKES AND 'GATORS ARE SMALL FRY COMPARED TO VOLANNS. WITH THEIR POWERFUL JAWS AND AQUATIC AGILITY, THEY'RE MASTERS OF UNDERWATER COMBAT. OUT OF WATER, THOUGH, THEY QUICKLY DRY OUT.

A BAD TIME TO GO RIPJAWS:

ON DRY LAND, RIPJAWS IS OUT OF HIS ELEMENT AND BASICALLY USELESS.

A GOOD TIME TO GO RIPJAWS:

IN WATER, RIPJAWS WILL GET THE BETTER OF ALMOST ANY OPPONENT.

HOMEWORLD: PISCCISS

A TURBULENT OCEAN WHERE THERE'S ALWAYS A BIGGER FISH LOOKING FOR DINNER!

SCALE

BEN   RIPJAWS

DESIGN AN ALIEN

THINK YOU COULD DO A BETTER JOB
THAN THE OMNITRIX? THEN DESIGN YOUR
OWN ALIEN! MAKE IT AS SCARY, CRAZY OR
FREAKY AS YOU LIKE ...

NAME: Sixarans time 20
SPECIES: to hold 3 objects atones to tell time
HOMEWORLD: Khafas tell time
POWERS: to use Super Strenth to kill By telling time

68

ANSWERS

THE RED OMNITRIX SYMBOLS ARE ON PAGES 13, 16, 18, 24, 30, 41, 48, 50, 52 AND 64.

PAGE 16
CRYSTAL MAZE

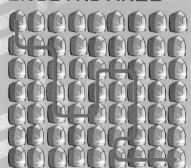

FREAKIN' OUT
B AND F ARE THE SAME.
(C IS MISSING THE ARM STRIPE AND D HAS TOO MANY FINGERS)

PAGE 17
NAME GAME
STINKFLY
SUDOTRIX

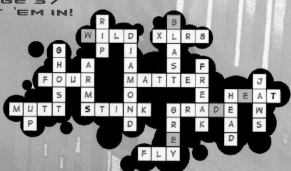

PAGE 22
10 OUT OF 10
1-C, 2-B, 3-A, 4-C, 5-B, 6-A, 7-B, 8-B, 9-C, 10-A

PAGE 23
SHUTDOWN
BOX 3 CONTAINS THE BATTERY.
THE NEED FOR SPEED

L	R	X	R	R	L	8	8
X	L	R	8	8	X	8	X
R	X	8	L	R	L	L	R
L	8	L	X	L	R	8	R
8	R	L	X	X	8	L	L
X	L	8	X	R	R	X	8
R	X	X	L	X	L	R	8
L	8	X	L	R	L	L	R

PAGE 36
WASHOUT
THE BLUE TOWER WILL PUT OUT THE FIRES.
PAGE 37
FIT 'EM IN!

THE EXTRA WORD IS 'DWEEB'.
WORD WARP
NAME, MADE, DEAD, HOME, DEMON, MOAN, DOME, HIDDEN, NOD, ODD, MINE, MEDIA ETC.

PAGE 48
TO THE RESCUE

PAGE 52
STORMFRONT
BEN MUST LAUNCH FROM THE TV TOWER.
PAGE 53
UP CLOSE
PICTURE D DOES NOT MATCH.
GROSS OUT!
THERE ARE 12 GRUBS.

PAGE 60
SPOOKY CHANGES

PAGE 61
WISH YOU WERE HERE?
Sorry if I've not written in a while! Yesterday we visited the Hiawassi Xylophone Museum – it was even better than I expected! It would be no lie to say it was the high point of our holiday. Then in East Ellijay I bought an enormous basket – who knew something made with reeds could weigh that much!

ADD 'EM UPGRADE!

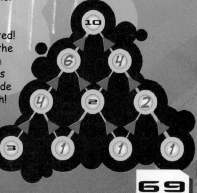